GW01018597

Handwriting

How to use this book with your child:

It is recommended that an adult spends time with a child while doing any kind of school practice, to offer encouragement and guidance. Find a quiet place to work, preferably at a table, and encourage your child to hold his or her pen or pencil correctly.

Try to work at your child's pace and avoid spending too long on any one page or activity. Most of all, emphasise the fun element of what you are doing and enjoy this special and exciting time!

Don't forget to add your reward sticker to each page you complete!

Reward sticker!

Designed by Plum5
Illustrations by Sue King, Sharon Smart and Andy Geeson
Educational consultants Chris Andrew and Nina Filipek

Autumn
Publishing

Shapes

Start at the dot and trace over the dashes to draw these shapes. Try to keep your pencil on the paper for the whole time.

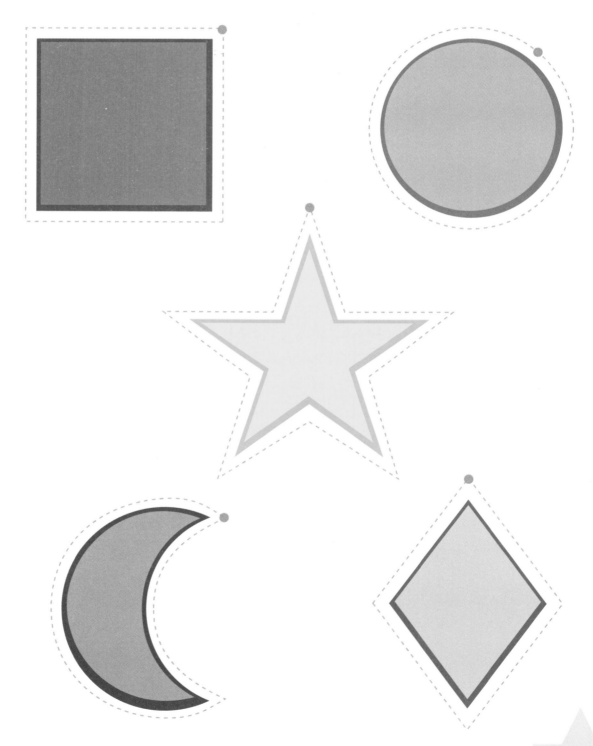

Reward sticker!

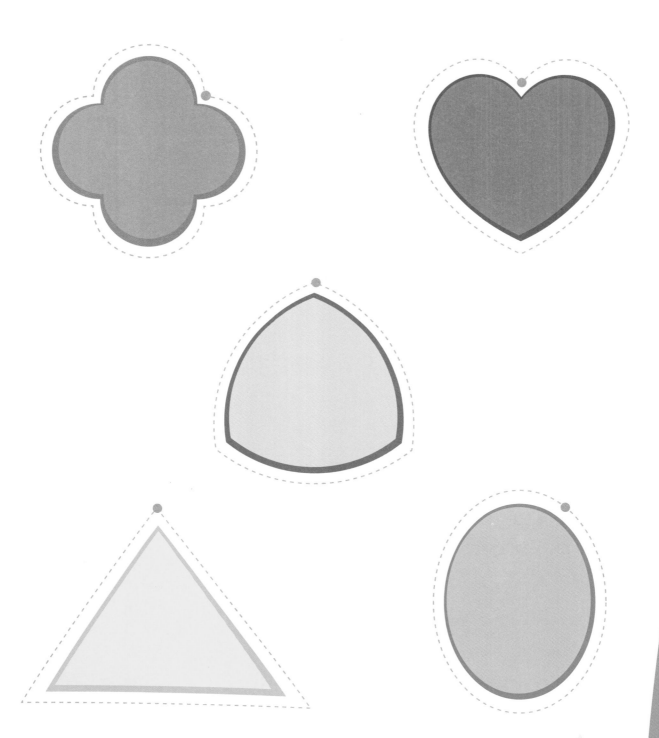

Writing patterns

Start at the dots and trace over the dashes.

Reward sticker!

More writing patterns

Start at the dot. Look at the direction of the arrows and trace over the dashes. Then write the patterns yourself.

Reward sticker!

MMM MMMMMMMMM

UUU UUUUUUUUUU

CCoo CCoo CCoo

Reward
sticker!

Letter patterns

Straight lines and curves

Look at the direction of the arrows and trace over the dashes.
Then write the letters yourself.

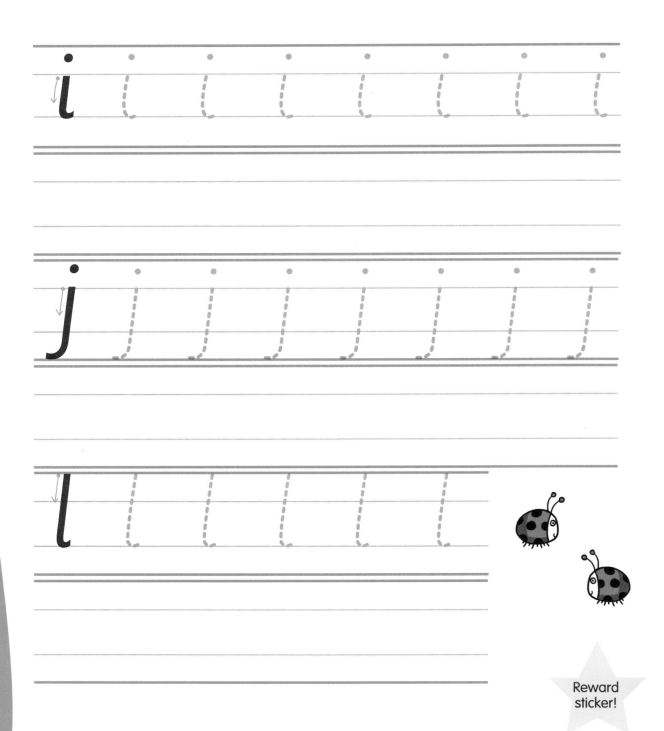

y   y y y y y y y y y y y y y

u   u u u u u u u u u u u u u

t   t t t t t t t t t t t

Reward sticker!

More letter patterns

Up and down strokes
Look at the direction of the arrows and trace over the dashes.
Then write the letters yourself.

h h h h h h h h

b b b b b b b b

p p p p p p p

Reward
sticker!

More letter patterns

Half circle and circle

Look at the direction of the arrows and trace over the dashes.
Then write the letters yourself.

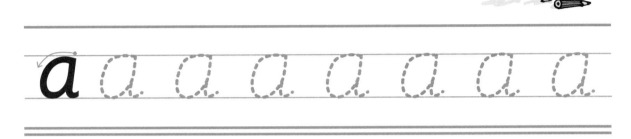

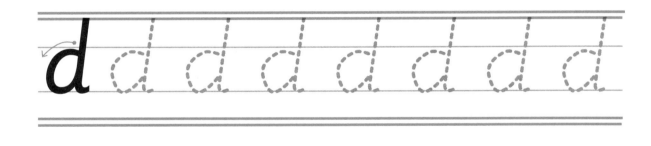

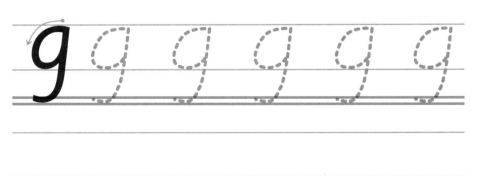

Reward
sticker!

12

c c c c c c c c

q q q q q q q q

e e e e e e e e

o o o o o o o

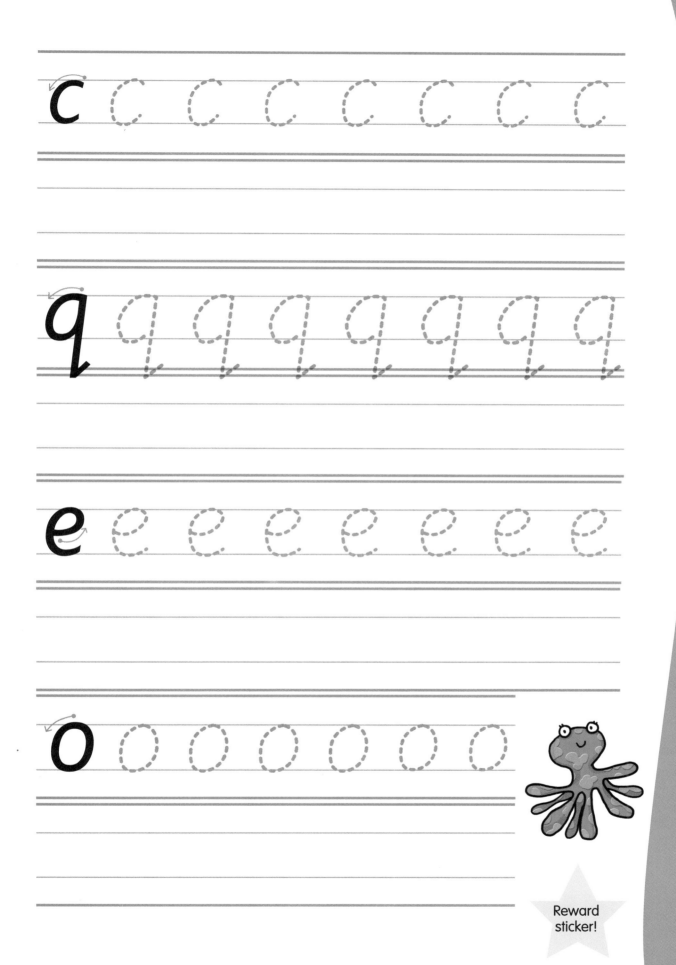

Complex letters

Look at the direction of the arrows and trace over the dashes.
Then write the letters yourself.

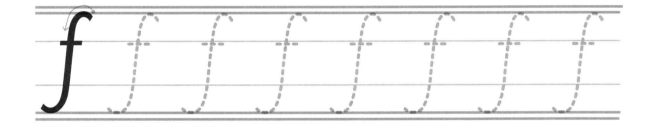

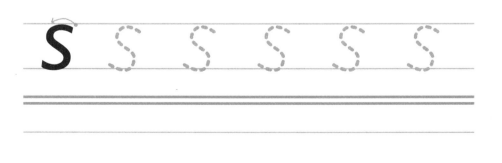

Reward
sticker!

z z z z z z z z z z z z z z

v v v v v v v v v v v v v v

x x x x x x x x x x x x x x

k k k k k k k k k k k k

Letter formation

Trace and copy the letters of the alphabet.

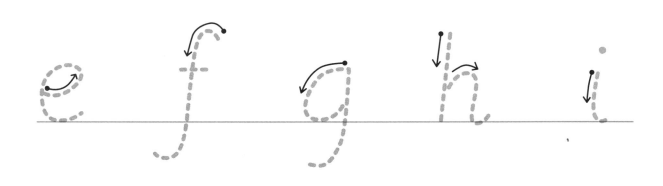

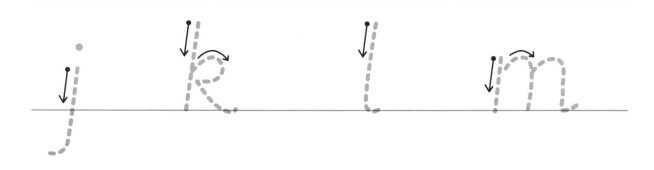

n   o   p   q

r   s   t   u   v

w   x   y   z

Reward sticker!

17

Joining strokes

To do joined-up writing you add **exit** strokes at the base of some letters. Trace over the dashes, then write the letters yourself.

i l k u m

i l k u m

n a d e t c

n a d e t c

Reward
sticker!

More joining strokes

Letters based on a half-circle or circle can have joining strokes at the **beginning**. Trace over the dashes, then write the letters yourself.

a   c   d   g   o   q

a   c   d   g   o   q

Practise:

ad   do   oc   ag

ad   do   oc   ag

Reward sticker!

More joining strokes

Some letters have exit strokes at the **top** of the letter.
Trace over the dashes, then write the letters yourself.

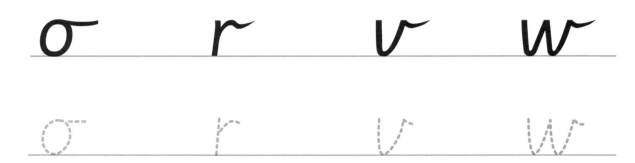

Practise:

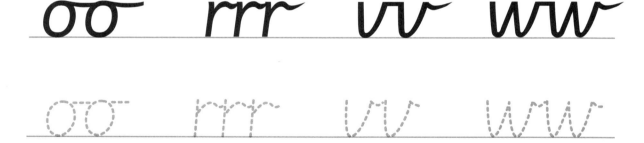

Reward
sticker!

More joining strokes

The letters **f** and **t** sometimes have different kinds of joining strokes. Trace over the dashes, then write the letters yourself.

f or f   f   f

t or t   t   t

fl   ef   tu   tr

fl   ef   tu   tr

Some letters can be joined with a loop, or they can be left unjoined.

g or g   j or j   y or y

g g   j j   y y

More joining strokes

This is how to join the remaining letters of the alphabet.
These letters can be joined or left unjoined.
Trace over the dashes, then write the letters yourself.

p   b   z   x   s

ph   br   bl

ph   br   bl

ox   box   zoo

ox   box   zoo

Reward
sticker!

Pairs of joined-up letters

Here are some examples of pairs of joined-up letters.
Trace over the dashes, then write the words on the lines.

poppy

kitten

lorry

moon

teddy

geese

Reward
sticker!

Practise joined-up writing

Copy the words on the lines under each picture.
Try to keep your pencil on the paper for each word.

a puppy and a poppy

a kitten and a mitten

Reward
sticker!

a moon and a balloon

a frog sits on a log

Capital letters

Copy the letters of the alphabet as capital letters.

Reward sticker!

N O P Q

R S T U V

W X Y Z

Reward
sticker!

Practise capital letters

Write the capital letters for the days of the week, and the months on the opposite page.

_unday

_onday

_uesday

_ednesday

_hursday

_riday

_aturday

Reward sticker!

_pril

_uly

_ctober

_ecember

Reward sticker!

Writing sentences

Write the sentences on the lines.

Children play in the leaves.

Leaves fall from trees.

Reward
sticker!

We love playing in the waves.

_____

Ice cream is lovely.

_____

Reward
sticker!

More writing sentences

Write the sentences on the lines.

Birthday cakes need candles.

_____

Then we blow them out.

_____

Reward
sticker!